# Livi Fibromyalgia Patients

*79 Ways You Can Make
Their Lives Better*

Tom Buford

# LIVING WITH FIBROMYALGIA PATIENTS

*79 Ways You Can Make Their Lives Better*

E-book edition Copyright © 2012 Tom Buford

Print edition Copyright © 2015 Tom Buford

Print edition ISBN: 978-0-9708103-1-1

A Quiet Place Media publication

Every patient should consult his or her own medical professional to learn the treatment that is most appropriate for him or her. Nothing written in this book should be construed as a substitute for professional medical advice. Although no medical treatments or prescription medications are recommended in this book, it would be wise to consult your physician before following the suggestions written herein. No two patients are alike. What works for one patient may or may not work for another. Therefore, the advice and suggestions written in this book may not be applicable to the fibromyalgia patient in your life. If a particular suggestion does not apply to you or your fibromyalgia patient, you should not consider that suggestion as appropriate for you or for that patient.

The author shall not be responsible for any damage or loss that is said to arise from any use of the suggestions in this book.

# Table of Contents

# Introduction

## Who this book was written for...

*Living With Fibromyalgia Patients* was written especially for you if you are in one of the following groups of people:

1) Families or friends of people who have been diagnosed with fibromyalgia and you do not understand the issues that FM patients have to deal with every day of their lives.

You just want to know more about the lifestyle changes you have seen in your own family member or friend and how you can perhaps help life to be a bit more bearable for that person.

2) People who have been diagnosed with fibromyalgia and have found it difficult to explain the ramifications of their illness in such a way that their families or friends can truly understand why and how life has changed for them.

Hopefully this book will be just the tool you need.

## What this book will do for you...

Within the pages of this book you will learn what life can really be like for fibromyalgia patients. You will learn what it is like for them to wake up and hardly be able to move their feet from the mattress to the floor, why they sometimes can't "get it together" before lunch time, why it seems that they have suddenly become forgetful, emotionally sensitive, and much more.

You will learn 79 things that family members and friends can do to help their fibromyalgia patients live better lives. You will learn real, practical tips for working around uncomfortable situations, helping the patient remain productive, fighting fibro fog, and more.

## Why you should listen to this author...

Tom Buford, the author of *Living With Fibromyalgia Patients*, is a man whose wife of more than thirty-eight years has suffered with the disabling effects of fibromyalgia for more than a decade. He knows first-hand what it is like to watch his wife change from one who earlier in life might have been seen on a lake riding a jet ski or climbing trees in a friend's yard to one who can hardly get out of bed some mornings, one who he has found sitting on her bed silently crying because there was no relief from the pain, even with heavy-duty pain medications.

Tom knows the empty feeling that comes with seeing his bride in obvious pain and not knowing what he can do to make her day more bearable, or if he is told what to do, may not think he knows how to do it in quite the way she needs it done. He knows what it is like for his wife to desperately need his touch, yet he finds it difficult to control his sometimes too masculine touch in such a way that it is not too heavy or even pain inducing for her.

It is important to understand that the patient is not the only person who is living with fibromyalgia. It has a way of becoming part of life. Therefore, the patient's family and, to some extent, her friends also live with it.

In this book, Tom shares what he has learned from his wife and others about what it is like to live with FM. He candidly tells you what life is like in his household. He will discuss some of the things that he does or has done in an effort to make life more enjoyable for his bride.

## What this book is not...

*Living With Fibromyalgia Patients* is not meant to diagnose fibromyalgia or any other syndrome or disease. It was written in layman's terms and with as little medical jargon as possible. It is a "how to" book for the families and friends of people who have already been diagnosed with fibromyalgia.

The author is not a medical professional. Your doctor or other medical professional is the only person who is qualified to offer medical advice. (If your physician or other medical provider seems to discount the reality of fibromyalgia, as some still do, find one that is familiar with it and who is qualified to treat it.)

The purpose of this book is not to give you every possible detail about fibromyalgia and the research that has gone into the illness. There are other books that do a very good job of that. However, it is important for people who are in the circle of friends or family of a fibromyalgia patient to understand at least the basics of what it is, what is known about it, and what its symptoms are. Most people have heard of fibromyalgia. But if they have not had close personal interaction with a person who suffers with the illness, they probably have little or no concept of how many different ways its victims can be physically impacted by it.

# A Short Primer on Fibromyalgia

In this short chapter I will give you just a basic explanation of the illness so that you will be better prepared to follow through on the information provided later in the book. I personally find it easier to understand what my Honey needs if I first understand what is causing the particular problem she is experiencing at that particular point in time.

## What fibromyalgia is...

Fibromyalgia is a potentially disabling physiological disorder which is usually classified as a syndrome (a group of signs and symptoms that are frequently seen together in patients, but which have no known cause).

One thing that all fibromyalgia (FM) patients have in common is the presence of painful trigger points. Those points —specific spots on all four limbs, hips, and the neck and shoulders—can be extremely tender or touchy and can present extreme pain when pressure is applied to them.

When my Honey first began to show symptoms of fibromyalgia, she would often mention that she felt as though she had the world's worst case of the flu. In addition to the generalized body aches, she would sometimes feel pain that was similar to arthritis. Once the diagnosis was made and we began to learn more about it, we saw that FM is actually quite different from arthritis. Arthritis causes damage in the joints. Fibromyalgia does not. While FM causes pain in muscles and connecting tissue, medical professionals say it does not actually damage the muscle. In my Honey's case, though, it has been shown to shorten muscles, which causes pain at muscle insertion points. Her muscles also tend to become filled with knotty lumps. She has been known to have joints dislocated because of abnormal muscle tension around them.

The jury seems to still be out on the exact connection, if there is any, between fibromyalgia and chronic fatigue syndrome. A high percentage of fibromyalgia patients have also been diagnosed with CFS. Conversely, a high percentage of CFS patients have also been diagnosed with fibromyalgia. Some researchers believe that both syndromes are part of the same illness. Others believe they are completely separate disorders with similar symptoms. The main difference between the two syndromes is that the diagnosis for fibromyalgia is centered on the presence of widespread pain, while the diagnosis for chronic fatigue syndrome is centered on the constant presence of severe fatigue. Only a physician who is familiar with both disorders can make an absolute diagnosis.

According to the (United States) National Institutes of Health, five million Americans age eighteen and older have fibromyalgia. Most of them—80 to 90 percent—are women. FM is not exclusive to women, though. Men and children of both sexes can also have it.

## What are the symptoms of fibromyalgia?

One thing that seems to be common among most, if not all, fibromyalgia patients is that their sensitivity to pain is greatly elevated. For some reason, their brains register pain at greater levels than the average person's would. For example, I might feel pain in my shoulder that I would rate maybe a three on a scale of one to ten. That exact pain sensation for an FM patient might be an eight or nine, or even off the scale in some cases. Everyday aches and pains that people develop normally as they go through life can be extraordinary aches and pains for FM patients.

I have seen my Honey wake up with extreme pain in different areas from head to toe. Today the pain may be centered in one or two locations. Tomorrow, it could be centered in two completely different places.

Pain sometimes seems to manifest from lying still. It can also show up hours after some extra activity that lasts longer than normal. She may feel pretty good and be excited to feel better. She then gets involved in some activity for which she will pay dearly the next day. Payment may be in the form of pain, or it may take the form of stiffness, tenderness, or extremely active hot spots (trigger points).

There are a number of symptoms that are common in fibromyalgia patients. Among them are:

Unusually high sensitivity to pain
Serious fatigue

Pain that shows up all over the body, even in unexpected places

Depression

Fitful or very light sleeping

Difficulty maintaining concentration

Forgetfulness

Muscles that feel overly tight or overworked even with light activity.

## What causes fibromyalgia?

I know of no one who has yet gone on record with a definitive, one size fits all, cause for fibromyalgia. Researchers are making progress, though. Studies have been done that look at the possibility that certain genes may be part of the answer. Other studies have looked at the flow of blood in the brains of FM patients.

An in-depth survey of the research that has been done into the causes of fibromyalgia is beyond the scope and purpose of this book. But, one theory is that certain types of external traumatic events may act as triggers, setting fibromyalgia in motion. My Honey was involved in an accident several years prior to her fibromyalgia diagnosis. A car struck her as she walked from the supermarket to her car. Her body went up on the hood of the car to the windshield and when the car stopped, she rolled back off the hood onto the concrete pavement. In her case, we believe that accident may have been an FM trigger.

Emotional trauma or life-changing stressful events may also play a role in the development of the illness. Stress can take a toll on anyone. But it can be a hugely aggravating force for fibromyalgia patients. I have personally seen the effect that stress has had on my Honey.

## Is fibromyalgia fatal?

No, fibromyalgia itself is not fatal. I have heard of cases where patients with this or other conditions did not find the encouragement they needed to make it through the disease or illness and, because of mental imbalances did one thing or another to cause their own deaths. But that is not the same as the illness itself being fatal. Fibromyalgia can definitely make life miserable for its victims, but it alone will not kill them.

## Is there a cure for fibromyalgia?

Not yet. There are a few medications that are prescribed for help in concentrating, muscle pain, nerve related pain, depression, sleep assistance, etc. None of them presents the patient with a cure, but they have been shown to be effective in masking some of the symptoms in some patients. We hope for the day that new research leads to a cure.

## Without a medical cure, can people who have fibromyalgia ever get over it?

I have heard of people who testified that they had overcome fibromyalgia. There are days when the symptoms subside for any person who has it, but I have not personally known of any for whom the symptoms completely and permanently disappeared. I sincerely hope there are people who can say that theirs have. If that is the case, life has most likely taken a dramatic turn toward the better for those people. If even one person can see a reversal, there is hope that others might also see the day when theirs goes into remission or disappears altogether.

## Common misconceptions...

One of the worst misconceptions is that fibromyalgia is not a real medical condition. A few years ago my Honey had a doctor who held that belief. Needless to say we did not go to him for help with her condition although we thought the world of him on a personal level.

It is very common for people to be told that what they feel is all in their minds, that there is no proof or visible evidence that what they are experiencing is caused by a real physiological occurrence such as a tumor, questionable blood test results, or verifiable nerve damage. Therefore their illness must exist only in their imaginations.

Fibromyalgia is a very real physiological condition for millions of people. The fact that there is not yet a specifically identifiable precursor or a specific blood test to verify the presence of fibromyalgia does not nullify its existence. There are other tests that are used to diagnose fibromyalgia such as examinations in which pressure is applied to eighteen specific tender points. A fibromyalgia patient will feel pain or tenderness in at least eleven of those points. There are other criteria, which if met, are combined with the tender point examination to make the final diagnosis.

# If Only They Understood!

*Be careful, don't run into things...*

There are times that I can see in my Honey's face the thought, "If only they understood…" when someone brushes against her or offers a hug that is a bit too tight. Fibromyalgia is a condition that is not visible to the eye. If you meet an FM patient at church or in the grocery store, you don't necessarily see obvious signs of probably painful conditions as you might if the person had rheumatoid arthritis or some other crippling disease. The patient may have some visible health condition in addition to fibromyalgia, but the FM itself does not manifest visibly.

## No china dolls

If you read every suggestion in this book and then mentally attach all of them to one person, you might go away with the idea that I see fibromyalgia patients as being overly fragile little china dolls sitting on the shelf of life, just one bump away from destruction. Nothing would be further from the truth. Most FM patients are incredibly strong and vital individuals. They are resilient people who have the same desires for social interaction, friends, and a physically active life that you and I have. The difference is that their fibromyalgia makes it much more difficult because of the restrictions that their bodies place on them.

The primary purpose of this book is to offer some valuable tools that you, as a family member or friend, can use to help your FM patient actually live the vibrant life that she wishes for.

## Things to remember when interacting with fibromyalgia patients...

In the next section you'll learn about some of the not-so-obvious things that fibromyalgia patients wish other people knew. As you read, realize that every fibromyalgia patient is different. Two FM patients sitting next to each other will very likely have different pain levels. Their physiological responses to pain will possibly be different. Some will have pain centered in certain parts of their bodies, while others will have head to toe pain on a daily basis. Some will have additional ailments to contend with alongside their fibromyalgia. Your FM patient may have to work around fibrofog for most of their waking hours while her FM friend hardly ever has it.

What you are about to read is a list of suggestions which you can follow and things that you should keep in mind as you live your life with a fibromyalgia patient. You may read a suggestion and think, "What the heck is he talking about?

I've never heard of half of these issues." But you may also be the one who reads the list and thinks, "Been there, done that! I've seen or heard about all of these suggestions. But why didn't he mention this or that other thing?" You may read suggestions that seem to be the same as one you read earlier. I have tried not to duplicate exact suggestions. Sometimes what you are seeing are suggestions that are similar but different and with different outcomes.

Your FM patient may be affected by just a few of the things you read, but not by others. A different patient could be quite the opposite and may be affected by many of them. Whichever group you fit into, there is something in the pages that follow which if heeded, will help you to help your fibromyalgia afflicted family member or friend to live a full and more joyful life. If that happens, I will have done my job.

One more thing before we get to the list of suggestions. I refer to your friend or loved one who has fibromyalgia as your FM patient. I refer to my wife, the FM patient in my life, as my Honey. You will see that I frequently refer to the fibromyalgia patient using the feminine pronoun her. I do that simply because 80 to 90 percent of people who have been diagnosed with fibromyalgia are women. The suggestions apply, however, whether the patient is male or female, young or older. I also use the terms FM and fibromyalgia interchangeably.

# 79 Ways You Can Make Your Fibromyalgia Patient's Life Better

## 1. Accept that fibromyalgia is real.

This one should go without saying, but sadly it can't. There are still doctors who have not accepted the reality of the condition. Granted, more and more are becoming convinced. But the first one that your FM patient needs to accept the reality of fibromyalgia is you! If those people who are closest to her do not accept that what she knows to be facts in her life really exist, the task of living with it becomes even more onerous. That in itself contributes to the stress she already feels and becomes just one more emotional burden for her to carry. Recognize that while they don't necessarily want sympathy, life is easier for them psychologically if they feel that their lives and their pains are accepted as real.

Be proactive - rest
before I really need to
(yes)

## 2. Understand that family plans can change suddenly. Be *flexible*

Plans change constantly for an FM patient. She may go to bed with plans to conquer the world the next day. She may see herself filling her bird feeders or repotting a houseplant. She may have every intention in the world to try a new recipe for dinner. But then, she wakes up the next morning and the reality of a new FM day slaps her in the face. The birds might find their feeder restocked. But the houseplant has to live another day in the old pot. The idea of a new dinner recipe is replaced by, "Honey, can you stop and bring dinner home tonight?"

See if the following scenario is familiar to you. Last night you and your beloved (who happens to be a fibromyalgia patient) made plans to get up this morning and raid the yard sales in the nice neighborhood across town. When you got through with that little jaunt, you were going to use the matinee movie tickets you had bought online.

You got up early, drank your pot of coffee so you'd have enough energy to keep up with her roaming from sale to sale. You read your morning paper, and while you were standing at the sink shaving, your beloved appeared at the bathroom door with that pained look that instantly made you wish you hadn't drank that pot of coffee.

No yard sales today. Movie might happen. Movie might not happen. But whether it does or not, life goes on. Plans change suddenly in the world of the FM patient. Learn to live with it. There is a certain freedom that comes from living spontaneously anyway. I can tell you from experience that it is better to come to the place where you can go with the flow without losing your peace than to grit your teeth on the inside and smile on the outside. She cannot help how she feels. But she needs your help to deal with her day and it starts by offering her a bagel and a cup of whatever she likes to drink first thing in the morning.

I can also tell you from personal experience that every day with a fibromyalgia patient is likely to be a bit different from the one before. There are things that start out somewhat the same—the wakeup routine, etc. But on your most intuitive day, you will probably not be able to completely plan a day's activities for you and your patient, and then see both of you follow that plan to a T. We have tried to plan out our days before and we still try to do it from time to time. But we've learned to go with the flow. Maybe I should say that my Honey has learned to go with the flow and I have learned to watch the flow go by and occasionally step into it.

It does not work for me to try to force my routine on her. She doesn't try to force her routine, such as it is, on me either. But we do try to have things that we can plan on doing together throughout the week. For instance, we always try to plan out sofa time on Mondays to watch Antiques Roadshow reruns, on Thursdays to watch a local show about things to see and do in our home state (even though we never go see or do any of the things they talk about), and on Saturdays to watch the one thousandth rerun of *Keeping Up Appearances* on Public Television. (You can see that we are pretty much a hyper-active couple.) Beyond that, life is a toss-up, partially due to our ages.

We wake up each day with an idea of what we want to have happen, then at the end of the day, we may or may not look back to see how much of it never actually transpired. If you have things that you would like to do, and your patient has no interest in being part of them, then figure out a way that you can do them alone while still giving your patient whatever she needs. If the plan is to do something that both of you like to take part in, you may have to be more flexible.

I wish I had a five dollar bill for every time my Honey has canceled an appointment with one of her doctors because she just did not have the spunk in her to make it. She is forced to make it to some appointments - for example, those that she has to keep to get her medication prescriptions extended. But if the appointment is for some type of therapy or other "non-essential" treatment, she sometimes has to cancel or postpone the appointment. It may sound counterproductive to cancel appointments that could potentially help her to feel better. But sometimes she feels that the struggle to get there negates any benefit she might have enjoyed from having made the appointment.

The point is not to do away with the all of the routine day to day activities of a normal life, but to be prepared to do some of those things in a different way, on a different schedule, or perhaps some of them, not at all. Priorities change in life, and nowhere are those changes more evident than in the life of a fibromyalgia patient. Since you are now a part of such a life, you may find that your own priorities change as well. And that may not be such a bad thing either!

# 3. Be prepared to change social plans.

It is not just bird feeders, plants, and recipes that take a back seat to fibromyalgia. For many FM patients, social plans are tentative until the time for the event actually arrives and they make the decision to go or stay home. More than once, we have had to cancel plans for dinner with friends because my Honey just simply could not handle it. It has nothing to do with the desire to be with the friends we had planned to meet for evening. My Honey can dearly love someone and spend the days leading up to the date of the dinner or other event planning what to wear, or maybe even deciding on a little gift for someone in the other group. But when the day arrives, she is not be able to deal with getting dressed up, making the ride to the restaurant, the noise level in the restaurant, and the general hyper energy that can be a part of such activities. She, like other FM patients, often needs quietness when her energy levels are low.

There is a tendency in some families to place more importance upon social events and interactions than on family events. They are seen as having more potential impact on job security or social standing. To some extent, those perceptions are probably warranted. But in the family that has been touched by fibromyalgia, especially in severe cases, a change in the social mindset might be necessary. The first, and probably most difficult thing for some men to do, is to park their pride next to the curb and insert their FM patient's needs where pride once was. If it is absolutely necessary, if missing the event will have a financially devastating effect, then go on without her and unapologetically state that she just wasn't up to the physical strain that the event would have placed on her. Sacrifices are necessary at times. And after a while, if you have a deep love for your FM patient, you will most likely come to the place where you no longer see such last minute changes as sacrifices, but as one of the things that you gladly do in order for her life to be more bearable and joyful.

## 4. Recognize that energy levels rise and fall.

She may be ready to take on the world in mid-morning and completely drained by lunch time. Therefore, don't be surprised at what you may think are simply mood swings. They are more likely related to her energy level.

## 5. Be conscious of sudden movements and jolts.

Most fibromyalgia patients live with muscles that constantly feel sore—from a feeling of minor bruising to one of having been physically beaten. Like my Honey, some say they often feel as if they have the flu. The soreness changes from day to day or even from one hour to the next.

I've done it. You've done it. Everybody has done it. We have something on our minds. We're on a mission to get somewhere quickly. We get the world's worst case of tunnel vision. Then, without giving a second thought to where we are going, we physically bump into someone. That scenario happens so commonly that we hardly take notice, as when two people try to pass through the same doorway at the same time.

But when we live with or around a person who has fibromyalgia, we have to notice. FM patients can be very sensitive to abrupt movement, jolts, jarring, rough rides, or sudden contact of any kind. When someone bumps into an FM patient, her body will probably instinctively jerk and tense up as a protective reflex. That jerk multiplies the sensation of pain, sometimes for a short time and sometimes for an hour or more.

In this hurry up world that we live in, it can take some serious practice to get the hang of it, but we have to develop a habit of trying not to bump into people, especially if we know they are living with fibromyalgia.

"Not just physical jolts (no) the inner ones are worse then the physical ones

3/23/22
Even after years there are still times when it seems I still haven't got thru my head that I have 2 major illnesse (no, you haven't

## 6. Don't become irritated if your FM patient can't sit or stand for more than a few minutes.

Sitting in one position for more than twenty or thirty minutes is a real struggle for many fibromyalgia patients. I have found this to be true of my Honey, as well. It really doesn't matter if we are in a theater trying to take in a movie or driving down the road. About every half hour or so, she just has to stand up and move around. We can be visiting friends or family, and in the middle of the conversation, she has to stand up. To outsiders looking in, it could appear that she is trying to leave or is intentionally inattentive. But that is not the case. She is in survival mode. If she is going to survive the visit without paying for it later with additional pain and muscles that don't want to relax, she'll have to do it on her own terms. It was quite some time before I understood what was truly going on when my Honey would just get up in the middle of a television program that we were supposedly serious about watching together. She would get up and roam around the living room doing one thing or another, unintentionally leaving the impression that she was no longer listening to the program. Then one day, she got through to me that she was up and moving simply because she could not bear to sit any longer, even though her total sit down time had been maybe just twenty or thirty minutes.

Don't be surprised if you have a similar experience. Your FM patient may just suddenly (that is, as suddenly as FM patients can) jump up and walk around at what you think are the most inopportune times. And they may just as suddenly get tired of standing up and decide to park next to you on the sofa again. Think nothing of it. What you are seeing is their way of coping with one or more types of pain, muscle stiffness, or other discomfort.

# 7. Don't use your "I've already told you that" card.

You may have heard people say that they had the memory of an elephant. I'm not sure how great an elephant's memory is. I've never asked one. But I can tell you that it is likely that your FM patient may exhibit the opposite when it comes to short term memory. She may be able to tell you what every person at your wedding thirty years ago wore, but not remember something that you told her yesterday. She may be able to describe how a fragrance that you bought for her birthday ten years ago smelled, and even what the bottle that it came in looked like; yet not remember that you told her last night that you needed to drive across town for some errand.

Know this, she is not ignoring you. She is not pretending to listen, and then showing that she really wasn't. She is exhibiting one facet of fibro fog. Learn to live with it. If you have to tell her again, just do it—peacefully, calmly, and as if it were the first time you told her. She needs you to be really good at it.

## 8. Be ready to help look for lost keys.

Everybody I know has lost something, somewhere, sometime. I've spent five or ten minutes looking for my belt before I realized that I was wearing it. I've heard it said that we usually find things in the last place we look for them!

If your FM patient is anything like mine, she will need you to help her keep up with things from time to time. She may forget where she laid her keys, although she had previously religiously hung them in a certain place. She may lose her cell phone—two or three times a day. If that happens, just help her find them. After a while you may notice where she lays certain things that she will most likely not be able to find later. You would be doing your patient a huge favor by placing that item—cell phones, keys, or whatever it is—in a conspicuous place where you are at least "almost positive" that she will see them. By doing so, you help eliminate a great deal of stress from her life, and that, believe it or not, can go far in helping her to have a less pain-filled day.

## 9. Recognize that the look you see on her face may have been put there by pain, not by something you did.

Have you ever said something to someone and that person return your statement with a look that seems to say that you have somehow gotten under her skin? You have no clue what you just said that didn't sit right with her, but it seems obvious that something didn't. That sometimes happens around our house.

It is a fact that, being the human that I am, I have the ability to annoy my Honey. I can say things wrong, not respond to external signals properly, and all the other things that people who are among the breathing occasionally do. I can be in my world and not be paying enough attention to her world, and when the two worlds collide, apologies usually come tumbling out.

But that is not what I am talking about here. My Honey is the greatest prize I've ever won. She helped me to learn something about that unsettling facial expression that I sometimes mistakenly take as anger, frustration, or confusion after I say something. It is a four letter word. P-a-i-n. When her pain level is roaring around somewhere up in the stratospheric range, she cannot help but let it show. Remember this, FM husband or friend. Pain can contribute to all kinds of mixed signals and fouled up communication.

Don't always take her facial expression at face value. Perhaps on a perfect, pain-free day it might mean that you have stepped across some invisible line with your comments or demeanor. But on a raging pain day, it could just mean, "Hug me."

## 10. Help her find tables and seats away from air conditioning vents and fans.

A few days ago, my Honey and I went to a restaurant for dinner. The particular restaurant we went to is one where you walk up to the counter and tell them what you would like on your plate, then go find a table and wait for them to bring it to you. We looked for a table and thought we'd found one, but the air conditioning was blowing a little too hard from the ceiling. I pointed out another table and the waitress followed us. Before we sat down, my Honey spotted another table that she thought would be better. The waitress followed us and kindly placed our food on the table. I don't know what the young lady who was carrying our food around the dining room thought. But what my Honey would want her to know is that fibromyalgia patients normally cannot stand to sit where vents or fans are blowing on them. The muscles in my Honey's body will begin to physically tense up if she has to sit in such a place. The practice of scouting out warmer tables is just a preemptive strike against unwanted tension and pain.

Once she feels her muscles tightening up, it is very difficult for her to convince her body that it is time to relax. She is great friends with her electric heating pad. They spend quite a lot of good time together. Even on warm days, it sometimes takes additional help to coax her muscles to loosen up. She will often ask me to gently squeeze her shoulders, or rub certain spots on her body in hopes that the additional blood flow will lead to relaxed muscles.

# 11. Don't squeeze her hands or shake her arms.

Even a pat on the back can be painful to an FM patient. Because she can be easily hurt and her sensitivity to pain is so extreme, even the thought of being greeted energetically by a friend can be a source of dread. The fibromyalgia patient can dearly love the person walking toward her, but knowing that the forthcoming forceful hug and back patting will be terribly painful causes her to want to avoid that part of the greeting. Some people by nature will shake another person's hand forcefully, which in some cases is more like shaking the person's entire arm. They do so in love, but without the knowledge that while they shake and hug, they are providing the spark that will soon become a fire of persistent pain in their FM patient friend's body.

If you are the huggy feely type and cannot help but yield to the magnetism that draws you to greet your friends or family members exuberantly, try to remember that you should probably throttle it back just a little when it comes to your FM patient. She will love you for it, and I promise you that she will go on through her day with no doubt in her mind that you totally understand.

The hint that fibromyalgia patients normally cannot bear to be hugged vigorously or to have their hands shaken too exuberantly should not be taken as a suggestion that you not hug your FM patient. The need for personal contact is built in to most people, and FM patients are no different.

There are times that a gentle reassuring hug could be the perfect antidote for a miserable or painful day. While she cannot bear to be rubbed too hard, my Honey loves to be hugged gently, yet firmly. She loves to be held closely, although finding a position to do so without bringing on other discomfort can be a challenge.

## 12. Recognize that deep reaching, such as removing clothes from a washing machine can be painful.

As you have probably already gathered, experiencing life with a fibromyalgia patient is about learning how the normal things in life bring on abnormal responses in her body. A simple thing like reaching deep into a washing machine to remove wet clothes is a perfect example. You may see your FM patient empty the machine without apparent complications on several consecutive laundry days. Then one day you come in from work and find her rubbing her shoulder or arm muscles. It may be her back or some other body part. This time, the washing machine sneaked up on her and snatched her out of her comfort zone. Wet clothing is heavy. In some laundry machines it is a long way to the bottom of the tub. That combination of factors may be all it takes to cause severe pain and to fire up her trigger points.

My Honey still uses the same top load washing machine that we bought several years ago when we moved into our present home. But I often see signs in her that we need to consider making our next machine a front load machine installed a foot or so above floor level so that she can easily avoid the strain of standing on her head in the old washing machine every time she has to empty it. You might want to consider some changes like that if you have machines around the house that require deep reaching and tugging in the normal course of using them. If changing appliances is a financial burden that you are not prepared to take on, then do what I should do more often. Offer to do the laundry for her!

## 13. Don't give her too many "to dos".

"Honey, would you run to the post office right quick for me? And while you're out, maybe you can stop by the home improvement store and pick up that air conditioner filter. And..."

Not so fast! If the fibromyalgia patient in your family is like the one in mine, she loves to do things for you. My Honey doesn't mind doing whatever I need done. That is, mentally. But physically it is a different matter altogether. If it is a "normal" day for her, she will want to get her driving behind her because she cannot handle sitting in the car for too long. Long lists (lists with more than a couple of items) stress her out at times. Add to that the city traffic, cranky customers in front of her in the checkout line, and the fact that after doing what I've asked her to do, she won't feel like doing any of the twenty-three things on her own list. That is the perfect recipe for stress, which leads to physical tension in her body, which leads to more pain, which leads to time on the heating pad.

You get the point. If you have something that you really need your FM patient's assistance with, by all means ask her. In her heart, she probably loves nothing more than doing whatever she can to take part of your load from you when she can. But physically, she can get to the point that her body screams just at the mental suggestion that it might have to over-exert itself.

Don't give me too many to dos

38

## 14. Get used to sleeping with lots of pillows on the bed.

This is one of those suggestions that at first glance may have you asking what it has to do with fibromyalgia. As I stated before, every FM patient is different. The one in my family has to sleep with a stack of pillows. She has some peripheral medical issues that force her to sleep with her knees elevated. But in so doing, FM-related factors start popping up that cause her to have to use a variety of different pillows under her neck or head throughout the night. She will sleep on one little pillow for a while, then she'll wake up and swap that one out for another oddly shaped little pillowette (is that a word?). Some of these little sleep aids she has bought, others are her own creations, straight from the seed bed of necessity.

Your FM patient may be able to get along fine with one pillow. And that will be a good thing because I can tell you that having all those extra pillows in bed is like having the bulk of three people in a two-person bed. But I'm not complaining. We have to do what we have to do. I'd rather buy more pillows than see her hurt because something didn't get propped up properly.

## 15. Become adept at mattress shopping.

To be honest with you I don't know how many years the average family sleeps on a mattress. My parents kept the same mattresses forever, it seemed. My Honey and I kept our mattresses for a long time prior to the arrival of fibromyalgia. Now, discussions about different mattresses are more frequent. We bought the one we currently sleep on not too long ago and already we are discussing what mattress might be better for her. Do we buy a mattress that allows each person to adjust his or her side of the bed separately? Do we buy a very expensive foam mattress and hope we can keep it long enough to get our money's worth out of it? Or do we hang in there with the one we have for a while?

Your mileage will vary, but be prepared for some low mileage mattresses at least until you find that one with the magical power that causes you to stop looking for another replacement.

## 16. Try to help her pace herself so that she doesn't pay for it the next day.

It is very easy for a fibromyalgia patient to over exert herself without realizing it. I have seen that happen many times with my Honey. She will feel like taking the world by the tail, and will go out to tinker with her flower bed or something else. A few hours later it is written all over her face that she had over-stepped the boundary between what she should have done and what she wanted to do. I have started trying to slow her down if I sense that she is pushing it too hard. With enough time, you will probably be able to gauge with your FM patient's activity as well.

## 17. Don't insist on heavy dishware or cooking utensils.

I won't bore you with all the details, but my Honey and I have had many more than one discussion about dishes and cookware. Those discussions usually center on the fact that many of the dishes in our cabinets—dishes that have been here much longer than FM has—are too heavy for her to handle now. Sometimes the discussion has to do with how the dishes are placed in the cupboard and whether there is any ergonomic sense to the madness that presents itself when we open the cookware door.

I put a particular skillet in a certain place within the stack for what I think is a logically sound reason. But my logic and her FM body have nothing to do with each other. So my Honey's body logic prevails. And that is okay. Combine their weight with high shelves or cluttered storage systems that require one to basically disassemble the cupboard just to grab a pot to boil water in, and you get a recipe for frustration, unnecessary stress, and avoidable pain. Glass dishware and some cookware can be heavy. For example, we would love to be able to use porcelain coated cast iron cookware, but it is far too heavy. Glass lids on cookware are a no-go as well. We have a set of ceramic dinner ware. But it rarely sees any use except for a backup. It lives on the top cupboard shelf, out of the way.

The plates and pots and skillets and spatulas need to be of a weight that she can handle and they need to be stored in such a way that she can comfortably reach for them. We keep an eye out for lighter, but durable and long-lasting kitchenware. You might want to do the same.

## 18. Be prepared to be the dishwasher guy.

The kitchen can present more concerns to the fibromyalgia patient than just where to put the pots and pans and how heavy the plates are. In my Honey's case, reaching above shoulder height repeatedly or with more than just a few ounces of weight is a no-no. If she ignores the past and goes ahead with it, she will soon be rubbing hotspots and reaching for the ice bag to cool them down.

My Honey has a light weight kitchen step that she can move around to help her see and reach into the upper cupboards. She has what she calls her reacher—one of those light weight tools that you squeeze a handle on one end and pick things up with the other end. You sometimes see people picking up trash along the roadside with a similar tool. She can use her reacher to retrieve something small that only weighs a few ounces. But it does not help with emptying the dishwasher and storing the dishes away.

The dishwasher and I have become very close. It washes whatever I put into it. I empty it and put the dishes away. Then we (mostly I) refill it so that it will have something else to do. The cycle continues, with much more frequency than most two person families, I suspect.

## 19. Understand that refusal to hold your hand is not personal.

My Honey loves to hold my hand while we walk through stores, to and from the car, etc. We are a very close couple. She is a romantic at heart. But her heart has nothing to do with what her body needs in order to live the best it can without pain. The natural swing that arms do when people walk is usually more than she can handle. Sometimes just that loving, innocent will act can be enough to set some of her trigger points on fire.

Just remember that in the absence of some other personal conflict between you, when your fibromyalgia patient pulls her hand away from your grasp, she is not refusing you or pushing you away. She is gathering her body parts up close to herself so that she can have a more balanced stride while walking. Sometimes she needs that individual arm swing. What she needs at any given time depends upon which muscles are pulling.

# 20. Help her relax her muscles.

Relaxing can be a real trick for any of us, especially with the ever-present rushing blur that cosmopolitan life has become. My Honey and I have a few favorite places to shop. Whenever we go to one of them, one of us will usually gravitate toward the music section where we will look for relaxing music by such instrumental artists as Steve Halpern, Kavin Hoo, or others similar to them. We have found that certain types of music are helpful in relaxing. We tend to prefer instrumental music played on piano, cello, or acoustic guitar. I recommend that you not settle for music that does not genuinely relax you.

My Honey normally spends some time at night just before bedtime lying on a mat on the floor with the lights off and some kind of soothing music playing in the background. This ritual helps her body and mind to relax and to become better prepared for sleep. It is about turning off the rest of the world and putting the day behind her.

Sometimes music is not enough, though. When it is not, she will sometimes ask me to massage certain areas of her body with the hope that I can help her tight, hardened muscles to loosen up. Sometimes she will ask me to work on some of her trigger points. That particular activity involves pressing down on a trigger point so hard that I feel certain that I must be causing more intense pain than that pain which she is trying to relieve.

I try my best to do those things precisely as she needs them done, but because I am not inside her body feeling exactly the pinpoint location of the trigger point or hotspot, it can be tricky for me to nail it exactly as she needs it. She will let me know to move left just a hair, or up, or down, or wherever it is. Her physical therapist has shown me some things that I can do for her and I am getting better at those. But I can tell you that it takes practice and careful attention to the signals that your FM patient sends to you. Like me, you may not nail it every time. If I am tired I find it more difficult to sense exactly what her muscles need. But with more practice, you and I will both become more proficient at sending at least some of the pain down the road.

## 21. Understand that she may constantly feel that she is behind in her work.

My Honey often tells me that she is behind on her work. Usually she has a list of things in mind that she wants to get done. She may not tell me what they are, but she knows. On those days that she feels that she is behind, it seems to me that she has just taken far longer to accomplish a task that she sees as a simple one. I attribute this feeling to fibro fog.

Catching up may be only a dream for her. Whether she is actually taking longer than she should is really beside the point. She feels that she is, and that is all that counts because it is her feeling of being behind that contributes to additional stress in her body.

There is one thing that I personally believe frustrates my Honey more than she lets on. That is the short attention span that many FM patients have. To be sure, there are tens of thousands of people who have been diagnosed with attention deficit disorders of one type or another. What happens with some FM patients is that they can't seem to keep their thoughts collected in one place long enough to see a task through. To borrow a term from the vernacular of the southern United States, they often feel "scatter-brained."

There are medications that can help some patients stay more focused. My Honey has tried some of them and has found them effective, although in some people they may have a variety of possible side effects. I am not medically trained and do not recommend particular medications to anyone. That would be something for your FM patient to discuss with her physician.

## 22. Encourage her to keep up her exercises and stretches, even when you are not so sure they help her.

One might think that exercising, if it helps at all, would offer a permanent benefit to FM patients. We tend to think of exercise in terms of a muscle building activity or as a cardio/pulmonary strengthening tool. In addition to those potential benefits, there is another way that exercise helps fibromyalgia patients. It acts like a maintenance device by keeping blood flowing through the muscles, thereby keeping them from becoming more toxic than necessary.

While you may not see a difference in her from your position, understand that maintenance - stopping any worsening in her condition - is important and exercise helps her to do that. Too much exercise, or even a little bit of the wrong exercise can be disastrous, but so can zero exercise.

## 23. Be willing to car shop.

My Honey is a spunky, spontaneous spirit. If she had her way she would be riding jet skis and climbing trees. (Well maybe she wouldn't at her age.) She would drive some type of little red sports car, maybe even a Volkswagen bug if its designers could remember what a VW bug is supposed to look like. But, like a lot of other things that have changed in our lives, so too has the type of car that she drives.

Instead of that rambunctious little sports car that she sometimes has dreamt of, I've had to buy her a larger car that some people might classify as a boat. Smaller cars just simply do not ride softly enough for her to be able to ride more than half a mile in them. My SUV is more than she can take on her average day. Your FM patient's particular situation may not require a different car, and if that is the case, I'm glad.

Factors such as how cold it is outside when she sits down in her car, what kind of seats she has to ride in (she cannot safely climb into or out of seats with leg bolsters on the seat cushion), and how well the car handles bridge joints in the highway are all factors that impact our car buying decisions now. My Honey cannot handle frequently sliding in and out of seats with fabric covers so I bought one with leather seats. To help her have the best day possible, I bought her a car with heated massaging seats (without leg bolsters), a heated steering wheel, and with radio controls and other frequently used controls that can be used without extended reaching. So that she would not have to walk out into the cold once to warm up the car, then again when it is time to leave, I bought her present car with remote starting so that she can start it from inside the house and walk out one time to a car with a warm steering wheel, warm seats, and warm air inside. Yes, it does have security features that require the doors to be locked before starting. Even if someone were to break into the car, they could not drive away in it unless they had the ignition key.

Pushing and pulling actions like using the mechanical type controls for tilting the steering wheel work against her, so this car has electric tilt and telescoping action on the steering wheel which she can adjust by touching a button rather than pulling on a stiff handle or knob.

One more thing that she has in her car that has been helpful is satellite radio. That allows her to choose a station that plays nonstop soothing music without the loud, tension inducing, blow you out of your seat advertisements that FM radio stations tend to play.

I hope your FM patient can drive and ride in a car that fits her personality, whatever it is. But if she finds that those cars just won't cut it anymore, perhaps a car with features similar to those that I have described might help.

## 24. If you go to a restaurant with seats that have no cushions, get in the habit of taking your own.

Personal seat cushions can be a fibromyalgia patient's best friend at restaurants or at event facilities where the seats have no cushions built into them. When my Honey's doctor told her not to sit on hard surfaces, we bought two of them. One stays in the house in case she just needs a little extra padding under her on those days that she has some computer time to put in. The other cushion stays in the car for those places where the management apparently believes that every person on earth is born with plenty of built-in cushion to handle their rough sawn plank benches and straight back wooden chairs.

Those seat cushions also come in handy on park benches. You know the ones where you can sit and watch the ducks swimming by and the geese stopping by to beg bread crumbs from you. Hint! Hint!

(See also suggestion 45.)

## 25. Get used to the fact that it may take her much longer to get things done now.

If you are a hyperactive, gotta get this done right now kind of person, you might find it just a tad bit uncomfortable to watch a person who has a severe case of fibromyalgia go about her tasks. To a person who works so quickly that it takes him ten minutes to do a job that the average person does in an hour, watching an FM patient do that task would be a bit like watching paint dry.

It might be helpful to remember that each of us is an individual. I do a thing one way. My Honey does it another way. Both ways accomplish the same end result, and unless there is some crucial time factor involved, just let her do it however she can manage it. And don't try to do everything for her, just because you think she is too slow about it or that you are helping her by doing it for her.

There is a line here that we probably need to think about. A couple of days ago my Honey was online trying to locate a USB cable for a particular brand of cell phone. I was working on my own things at my computer. I knew that she was spending quite a bit of time looking for this particular thing, but time gets away from all of us and I didn't pick up on the fact that my Honey was becoming frustrated because she had spent so much time on her quest. I often spend a long time trying to find the information that I am looking for.

To make a long story just a little shorter, I asked her the model number of the phone that she needed the cable for. She told me. I went to a search engine, typed in the phone's model number and the words USB cable, and got a list of places where the cable could be ordered. It frustrated my Honey terribly to see how quickly I had found the cable. Did that mean she was dumb or any other such derogatory thing? Absolutely not! It meant that she had tried in her own way to find it, and due to that day's high fibro fog rating (my own term—there is no such thing that you can look up), it was a very slow process for her. On another day, she might have found it in five minutes or less.

What I should have done was to be more attentive to what she was doing. Do my own multi-tasking: concentrate on what I am doing, and keep an eye on her progress in case she needs help at the same time. Had I done that, my Honey's frustration and stress levels would have been kept at a minimum, tension would have been lower in the room, and she could have gone on doing the other, more enjoyable things on her list.

## 26. Accept that medications which may knock you for a loop might hardly faze her.

I am one who can be very sensitive to medications when it comes to drowsiness, etc. There are medications that my Honey has been prescribed over the years that would knock me completely off my axis if I were to take them. However, she can take them and unless I had seen her take them or unless she had told me that she had taken them, I might never have known.

Do not be lured into thinking that the drugs that your FM patient's doctor has prescribed for her are not potentially dangerous. My Honey is very careful with her prescriptions. She monitors how many she has taken, what effects they had on her, and more. In the case of pain medications, if she can get by with fewer doses than the prescription allows, she skips a dose.

Occasionally, doctors will decide that it is in the best interest of the patient to change from one medication to another that is designed for the same purpose. Normally, the change works out fine. But, I can tell you from experience that it is possible for new or replacement medications to have unexpected side effects. That has only happened with one of my Honey's medications and her doctor quickly changed her to a different one. In that case, the unruly medication was supposed to help her get the deep sleep that all fibromyalgia patients need to rejuvenate their bodies. This particular one allowed my Honey to say things that were so far off kilter for her that I knew something was wrong. Shortly after that episode, she had a night in which she was up doing things that she had no memory of. When she told her doctor about it, he immediately took her off of that one and prescribed one that has proven to be safe for her.

The point here is that you may find that your FM patient has a very high toleration for all sorts of extremely powerful drugs. Please do not allow that toleration to lure you into a place where you don't notice behavior that could be dangerous or even life-threatening for her. She may bring a new prescription home one day only to find that she does tolerate it at all.

## 27. Learn to give her massages.

Massage is one of the most effective things that she can
have done. But it can also be detrimental if it is not done
correctly. The relaxing or sensual massage that you might
give a person who has no physical ailments could be quite
different from the massage that an FM patient needs for
therapeutic reasons.

If she asks you to give her a massage and you feel confident
that you can safely do so, then, go for it. I believe that some
people are more gifted than others in being able to sense
what a person needs during a massage. If you try it, but find
that you just can't pick up on all the right signals, try to ar-
range for her to have professional massages when she
needs them. You may feel badly for not being able to give
her the relief that she needs. I completely understand that. I
can sometimes do a semi-decent job of massaging my
Honey's problem areas, but at other times, I just don't have
it.

There is no shame in not being able to give a professional
massage. Fully qualified massage therapists go to school to
learn how to help their clients and patients. If you aren't the
right one for the job, there are trained professionals in your
area that might be a perfect fit for your FM patient.

One word of caution before you go flying out the door in
search of a massage therapist. Do your research before you

set the appointment. There are many well-trained massage therapists available. But they don't all have experience handling every physical ailment. The massage will be a better experience if it is done by someone who has experience with fibromyalgia patients, and especially if your FM patient is already familiar with the therapist.

## 28. Find a way to bring laughter into her life.

One of the best things you can do to help your FM patient have a better, more comfortable day is for you to come into her day with a sense of humor and a good mood. According to **HealthGuidance.org**[1] laughter has a huge effect on the body. Serotonin and endorphins are often called our feel good hormones. Laughter stimulates the body to release them and in the process, the person feels happy.

Elsewhere in this book I've talked about stress and its hugely negative effect on fibromyalgia patients. The good news is that laughter can have the opposite effect on the body because stress hormones run the other way when laughter shows up.

When stress is reduced, tension is relieved. Combine a reduction in stress with a reduction in tension, and then add to that the side benefit that endorphins have been known to help reduce pain, and you get an inexpensive drug-free way to reduce pain.

Anyone who has more than a basic cable television package has at their disposal a variety of comedy channels, movies, and goofy sitcoms that provide a good dose of laughter. In our city, the public library has quite a collection of videos that are available for check out. We will sometimes go through the collection at our local branch library and find something silly to watch, just for the purpose of putting stress and pain on hold and laughing for a while. Just to give you a free side tip, my Honey and I have found that the British have a view of life that is far different than the view that we Americans tend to have. Some of our hardest belly laughs have come while watching British comedy shows. If you haven't tried that, I suggest you do so.

(1) http://www.healthguidance.org/entry/11633/1/Positive-Effects-of-Laughter.html

## 29. Blame it on the weather!

Most people, whether healthy or not, are affected by the weather. On bright sunny spring or fall days, we tend to feel better in general and may be more upbeat emotionally. When the weather turns funky and the bright pleasant low-humidity days turn to dreary days with high humidity, heavy clouds, and either cold or very hot temperatures, our bodies tend to react and feel less comfortable.

Most people with fibromyalgia find that weather has an enormous effect on their pain levels specifically, and their comfort levels generally. I've never read any definitive research that says specifically how and why it happens, but the effects are accepted by the medical community as being true. I know that my Honey can tell when she gets out of bed in the morning if the weather has changed, especially when the change is from a day with high barometric pressure to one with low pressure.

For my Honey, and for millions of other fibromyalgia patients, pain will tend to be much more severe on days with low pressure and on days that are cloudy and humid. (Some patients say that they feel better on days that are not too dry, either.) Extremely hot or even slightly chilly days, combined with low pressure and humidity, contribute to muscle and joint pain. Many people report that they tend to have more headaches on such days, as well.

## 30. Consider moving to a place with more consistently comfortable weather.

My Honey has mentioned to me that she would love to live in a place where the weather is more consistently comfortable for her. We live in the southeastern United States where we see many days with barometric pressure that is lower than the level that is most comfortable for her. We get a lot of rain, a lot of humidity, and more than our share of stormy days. We don't have terribly cold unending winters here, but some fibromyalgia patients can have bad days if the weather is just cool and damp. My Honey is one of those patients.

At the present, our particular life situation does not permit us to make a move across the country, but if at some time in the future the right changes were to take place, we might consider making such a move. You might consider the idea for your FM patient if it is something you could do without wrecking your world completely.

## 31. Understand that you are not the only one who has forgetful days.

Have you ever had a day when it seemed that your head and the rest of your body had nothing to do with each other? I know that I have. In my case, it may just be part of the aging process, but it seems that more and more often I walk out the door on my way to somewhere and realize that the driving directions or my keys were still laying on the table inside. But directions are not the only thing that I've been known to leave behind.

I'll tell on myself one more time. A couple of years ago my dentist had a set of upper and lower partial dentures made for me. They are great. They look as real as I suppose they could. They are flexible and are probably as comfortable as I should expect any store bought teeth to be. I don't sleep with them planted in my mouth. Instead I plant them in their trusty little cup every night. A few weeks ago, I was two or three blocks down the street on my way to my day job when I realized that my teeth were home alone. I was on my way out in the wild, wild public with most of my teeth missing! Of course I turned around and retrieved them. I was a few minutes late for work, but I'm sure the higher powers at work had less trouble dealing with my tardiness than they might have had trying to look into my eyes rather than my semi-toothless mouth all day!

We all have days when forgetfulness seems to rule. But for the fibromyalgia patient those days can appear to outnumber days when everything goes smoothly and nothing gets left behind. My advice to you is to not give your FM patient a list a mile long of things that you expect her to remember to do for you. Writing them down helps, but does not guarantee that the list will be remembered or followed. The problem is that fibromyalgia patients have days when they are just mentally scattered. They have days in which they just cannot seem to concentrate on anything for more than just a short time.

Your FM patient's physician may be able to prescribe medications to help her better concentrate. Just be sure that she is aware of potential side effects before taking the medication.

## 32. You may need to let her stay in her bedroom and cry.

More than once I can remember not hearing my Honey puttering about the house. I would get up from my desk or wherever I was and look for her. I found her sitting on the bed in an unlit bedroom with tears streaming down her cheeks. When I asked what was wrong, she replied that she was just hurting and wanted the pain to go away.

Extreme pain can be emotionally devastating. It can bring on severe depression and a number of other issues. Sometimes my Honey experiences the desperation of not feeling that she is getting better. I'm sure other fibromyalgia patients have similar feelings from time to time.

If you walk into your FM patient's quiet place and find her crying from the pain and the sense that it just won't go away, you can try to comfort her. You can offer to hug her or to hold her for a few minutes. Sometimes that helps. Sometimes it takes nothing more than her being able to tell someone how she feels to get her over the hump and on with her day.

It would be a good idea to keep your eyes open for signs of depression. According to **WebMD.com**[2] approximately three out of every ten fibromyalgia patients had depression when they were diagnosed with FM. Depression seems to go along with fibromyalgia, possibly as an indirect result of the stress and social isolation that many patients experience. If you believe your FM patient is possibly clinically depressed, suggest that she see her physician, since depression can adversely affect how she manages her life and her physical condition.

(2) http://www.webmd.com/fibromyalgia/guide/fibromyalgia-and-depression

## 33. Get used to mood swings.

Guys, let me help you with something. If you've been married or in a relationship with a lady for any length of time, you've almost certainly butted heads with premenstrual syndrome, more affectionately known as PMS. You might have become acquainted with it simply because your mother also happened to be a lady.

Some women have a rougher time with it than others, but regardless how strong a lady's PMS is, it can be hard to miss if you are on the outside looking in. In spite of the view that comedians and television sitcoms might have you see, most women really don't want to be a holy terror during that time of month. It can be a sensitive subject for some women.

Your next question is probably, what does premenstrual syndrome have to do with fibromyalgia? The answer is basically, nothing at all. But what does have to do with FM is that sometimes a patient's mood swings, irritability, and certain other behaviors can be misunderstood as being PMS related. Fibromyalgia patients can experience frequent mood swings. Their moods can move from happiness to despair with no notice and with no apparent justification. They can go from jovial to verbally snappy and leave you wondering what you did wrong. The probable right answer is nothing. You may have done nothing wrong. Or you may have responded to a statement or question in a way that she understood incorrectly.

Be prepared for such occurrences. And know that it is not always her fault and that, in fact, it can be yours if you have not learned to be specific in your discussions and if you have not learned to be a good listener.

## 34. Realize that in spite of how she may act or present herself, she is probably thankful for the health that she does have.

There are days that my Honey, at least on the surface, thinks she could not possibly feel worse. But internally, she knows life could be worse—much worse. She wakes up and wonders what happened to her body during the night.

You've probably heard the old saying, "No matter how bad we've got it, someone somewhere has it worse." Don't rub that in to your FM patient, though. She knows it already. Let her feel the way she feels. If you sense the need to lift her spirits a bit, be creative about it. Perhaps you can suggest some activity that the two of you could do together that might take her mind off her agitated body for a while.

## 35. Understand that while her pain may get better for a while, it never goes away completely for most FM patients.

Your FM patient may have relatively good days when her pain level is reduced, such as days when she hasn't recently overworked her muscles, days when the weather is cooperating perfectly, and days when stress is at a minimum. I have never heard of an FM patient whose pain goes away for forever, though. If it did, a fibromyalgia diagnosis would no longer be appropriate. I wish that for my Honey and for the FM patient in your life. But until that days comes, realize that her pain, whether raging or relatively calm, never completely disappears.

## 36. Accept her restlessness.

This is not the same as not being able to sit or stand for more than 20 or 30 minutes (because of pain). If you have restless leg syndrome, you have a clue what her restlessness is like for her. FM patients frequently feel general discomfort in their limbs. There is the usual pain, of course. But there is also just an overall inability to feel "at home" in their bodies.

My Honey has told me that she sometimes wishes that she could get out of her body for a while. Your FM patient may tell you the same thing. If that happens, ask her if there is anything that you could do that would help her feel better. Don't assume that a massage or any other treatment would be the perfect solution. Remember that there are days that FM patients don't feel like being touched, even by trained massage therapists.

## 37. Get ready for nap time.

It is not a casual readiness, but a driving readiness. Nap now! I've seen this happen with my Honey. She would be sitting at her desk working, writing, or hanging out on Facebook when suddenly she just gets up and makes a nonstop trip to the bedroom.

Fibromyalgia patients frequently get very little high quality sleep, the vital deep sleep that helps their bodies rejuvenate. Sleep is vital for them. Most FM patients that I have had contact with require more hours of sleep than healthy people do.

To be truthful with you, I don't know that this urgency to nap is exactly an FM related thing, or if it is possibly more directly related to the medications that some fibromyalgia patients take. Whatever it is, when nap time comes, get out of the way!

## 38. Be alert for times when you can help her do something.

I know that we don't live in the 1950s. To people who live in this century, *Leave It to Beaver* and *The Andy Griffith Show* represent some form of life that probably had its start on another planet. In case it's been a while sense you've watched an episode of such ancient television programming, men opened doors for women and generally took care of the heavier lifting.

I am glad women have seen things change so dramatically for them. They've come a long way and there is still much work to be done.

In the case of fibromyalgia patients, being helpful is not about playing down to the weaker sex. It's about offering her the help she needs so that she can live a fuller, more enjoyable life. Remember that although I have used the feminine pronoun when referring to the FM patient in this book, they can be young or old, male or female. Whoever they are, ask if you can help do whatever it is that needs to be done. Maybe it is opening a heavy door. Perhaps it is doing the grocery shopping. Whatever it is, be open to clues that tell you when an opportunity to help is knocking at your door.

## 39. Ask her how she is feeling from time to time.

She may already be feeling that she talks about her aches and pains too often. Let her know it is okay. And while we are on the subject, practice your listening skills. If you are like me, you tend to listen on several channels at once. You hear the truck drive by the house, the dog barking down the block, the semi-interesting news story on the five o'clock news, a rerun of a conversation you heard at work, and your FM patient talking to someone who must be you since you are the only other person in the room other than her. And you try to convince yourself that you heard everything your FM patient was saying to you. Perhaps you heard the words. But conversation is more than words. It is a two-way street with auditory, visual, and emotional parts all rolled into one stream of thought.

We need to learn to ignore the truck in the street, the dog barking, and all the rest when our patients are talking. Their conversation may very well be more than them just wanting to talk to us. It may be that they need to talk. And if that is the case, we need to listen one hundred percent to them. It is important for them to be able to tell you how their day went, how they feel, and what frustrates them.

## 40. If you want to pay the FM patient a visit, call her first.

If you call to announce that you would like to visit with her for a while, and she says you are welcome to stop by, then, go for it. But, if she tells you that she just does not feel well enough for visitors that day, accept it and go on with whatever else you had planned.

Her refusal to accept your visit has absolutely nothing to do with her love for you. It is not her way of telling you that she thinks you are some crotchety old character or that she'd rather be visited by her screeching old Aunt Matilda. It just means that she may not feel like she has enough energy within her to deal with visitors. It may be that she had enough trouble just walking down the stairs to get her morning caffeine fix and trying to be a gracious host would just be more than she could muster at the time.

Don't take it personally. A few hours later might be different. Next time you call, she may be thrilled to have you stop by and she might even ask you to bring lunch with you.

# 41. Be willing to help her with therapy.

One of my Honey's doctors often gives her therapeutic exercises and stretches to do. He prescribes them to help her stay as limber as possible and to keep her muscles from tightening up. Occasionally she will be told to do something that requires more hands than she has, or that otherwise requires a second person to help her.

I admit that I am not as good at asking in advance if she needs my help as I should be. But I am always willing to help her if she asks me. Offer to help your FM patient with her therapy. I'm willing to bet that she would appreciate your doing so.

## 42. Offer to take walks with her.

My Honey's doctor tells her that walking is one of the best exercises that she can do, and that she should do it on a regular basis. She does try to walk when the temperature outside is comfortable enough. There have been times that she has asked me to walk with her. And I know that she would love for me to walk with her even when she doesn't ask. In her case, walking with her is a form of moral support.

Perhaps your FM patient could benefit from walking. Ask her physician. If he agrees that walking would be healthful for her, consider joining her. It might just be the boost that she needs to exercise and to get the blood flowing into her muscles.

## 43. Let her sound off.

Fibromyalgia patients sometimes need to vent a little bit just like anyone else. Let her. It's that simple. The chronic pain and other symptoms that she lives with can wear on her patience and her peace. She probably needs somebody to listen and you may be that somebody. Don't try to fix all her problems or tell her why she'd probably feel better about whatever it is if she'd just change her viewpoint. Just listen. Just be quiet and listen.

## 44. Try to bring a sense of humor with you.

Earlier I talked about the benefits of laughter to fibromyalgia patients. There are people who are bipolar or who have other disorders that affect moods or that cause drastic changes in temperament. However, moods for most people are not just good and bad, anger and joy. They normally fall along a continuum that ranges from gloom to exuberance, with most people falling somewhere in the middle.

Our job, as friends and family of fibromyalgia patients, is to try to bring a sense of humor along with us whenever we can. Moods, whichever end of the continuum they fall on, tend to fill the space where they are taken. If you take your joyful or funny mood to your FM patient's home, there is a strong chance that it will rub off on her. Conversely, if you go into her home dragging your "The world's going to hell in a hand basket" mood behind you, that can transfer to her as well.

As much as we can, we should choose to fill our spaces with humor. That act alone will help her more than you might know.

## 45. When you go to social gatherings, save a soft chair for her.

Padding is important for fibromyalgia patients, and not just the unwanted subcutaneous kind that many of us carry around with us wherever we go. Sitting on hard unpadded seats is a no-no for my Honey and many other fibromyalgia patients. Because of that, I have formed a habit of looking for padded seats when we go to social gatherings.

As in restaurants (see suggestion 24), sometimes there are no padded seats available. For situations like that we bought a wedge shaped cushion, similar to a stadium cushion that we can take with us wherever we go. It is light-weight and easy to carry. I purchased our first one at a local pharmacy but they are also available at other merchants as well.

## 46. Let her decide what's too much for her.

I've discussed elsewhere in this book how fibromyalgia patients may feel that they are not in control of their lives. Like anyone else, they want to be the bosses of their own lives.

If you know your fibromyalgia patient well, you may be able to tell when she is overdoing it. Unless there is an agreement between the two of you that you should tell her when you think she has reached her safe limit, I would suggest that you be very diplomatic about doing so. You don't want to see her hurt herself. And you certainly do not want to be pushy or to disrespect her right to do with her body what she wishes.

Consider your FM patient's personality and your relationship with her, then take that information and come up with better ways of suggesting that she back off a bit.

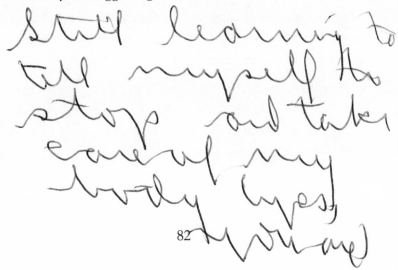

# 47. Don't assume how she feels on any given day.

As well as I know my Honey, and as adept as I have become at reading her body language and facial expressions, there are times that I completely miss the boat. I may take a look at her and believe that she is having a pretty good day. She may look in the mirror and know that she is having a day from hell.

Yesterday was just such a day. I know that my Honey rarely has a day that she is not in pain. I know that she keeps a lot of her feelings to herself. Sometimes she is doing that and I have no clue. She told me last night that her entire body was "flaring up." I could not see it on her face or in the way she walked, but it was true, nonetheless.

It is not safe to assume that you know how your FM patient feels if you have not specifically asked her. You may take a look at her and decide that she must be having a good day. She may, in reality, be feeling as though someone had beaten her with a baseball bat.

If there is some activity that you would like to do with her, ask her if she feels like doing it. If she does, go for it. If she doesn't feel like doing that movie or whatever it is, then ask her if there is something she'd rather do.

## 48. Don't rush her.

Whether it is when she is getting ready to go out or any other thing she is doing, rushing her just adds to her nervous overload. If you are like me, patience is not something that you wear like an overcoat. My Honey lets me know when I need to work on it. It is true that life for her is better when I live my own life with consistent patience.

My Honey needs to be able to live with as little outside pressure as she possibly can. I need to let my Honey take as much time as she needs and I'm willing to bet that you need to do the same for your FM patient.

Don't rush myself
(no,
don't)

## 49. Do not buy your FM patient a gift card to an unknown massage therapist.

I love to surprise my Honey with little gifts from time to time. Nothing brings me more pleasure than being able to give her whatever she needs or wants.

You may be like me in that regard. Knowing that massage normally is good therapy for your FM patient, you may decide to buy her a massage session as a surprise gift. Think twice and do a little research before you make that purchase. In our city therapeutic massages are available in gyms, hair salons, spas, chiropractic and family physician offices, and a hundred other places. Not all massage therapists are created equal. They don't all have the same training or skills. Some are skilled in the physical part of massage, but not so skilled in the art of listening to what the patient's body has to say.

The massage session will be a better experience if it is with someone who has experience with fibromyalgia patients, and especially if your FM patient is already familiar with the therapist. A session with the wrong therapist could have the opposite effect from what she needs.

I need to listen to my body ayes,
(you do)
Definitely need to
practice (yes you do)

## 50. Don't even think about surprising her with a party or tickets to a rock concert.

She would appreciate the thought, but the outcome of the evening could be quite different than you expected. Fibromyalgia patients are especially susceptible to sensory overload which could be in the form of being touched too much, loud music or ambient noise, certain types of lighting such as fluorescent, strobes, and more. When such an overload occurs, her symptoms can flare up dramatically.

An alternative is to offer her an evening out doing something of her choice. She might mentally wish that she could go to a concert when her favorite band from her college years comes to town, but know practically that doing so would be a bad move for her. Perhaps a quiet evening in a dimly lit restaurant would be better for her. Let her be part of the decision making process. The outcome will almost certainly be better.

The typical fibromyalgia patient prefers to be in control of her environment. She likes to be able to change it quickly if she needs to. She is likely to be uncomfortable in any environment that she cannot control. That could mean anything from the noise level, to the temperature, to the crowd size. In some situations, she could make a temporary change for herself by going to the powder room or somewhere else that is relatively quiet. Such places rarely exist at rock concerts. Even if the restroom is less noisy than the concert hall, the other concert goers who come in are likely to be overly excited and loud.

## 51. Remember that there are always things presenting themselves to her that she could once do, but no longer can.

Her inability to do them now can be a source of disappointment or even frustration. Consider that next time you think about suggesting that she use weights when exercising, walking the mall, riding a bike, blow-drying her hair long enough to get the result she really wants, carrying things that you know she used to be able to carry, or sitting until she is ready to get up rather than only as long as she can handle. Those are all things most people think nothing of, but which can be a strain for FM patients.

## 52. Help her get her ZZZs.

Fibromyalgia patients need several hours of uninterrupted sleep every night to help their bodies rejuvenate for the next day. Sound sleep is frustrated in the FM patient because constant pain makes sleep more difficult, yet deep sleep is crucial for physical recovery and pain reduction.

If your FM patient says that she needs to sleep, do what you can to make that happen. In our case, my Honey normally takes sleep aids that her doctor has prescribed. Yet she needs to go to bed early and get up late in order for her to have the hours of sleep that her body needs. Even with the medication, it is common for her to wake up every hour or so.

Uninterrupted sleep is vital. However, for my Honey, it can also be a kind of two-edged sword. On one side the longer, unbroken sleep is better at replenishing her system. She rarely experiences such a night. But when she does, she sleeps so soundly that she sometimes wakes up with more pain which she supposes is due to lying still and in one position all night.

To the extent that your particular lifestyle allows, try to help your FM patient get the rest that she needs. Every person needs sleep. For fibromyalgia patients, it is an absolute necessity.

## 53. Notice the restroom locations whenever you go to a public place.

Some fibromyalgia patients have serious problems with irritable bladders or with irritable bowel syndrome, issues that normal IBS medications don't seem to take care of. Some take medications that affect their digestive systems. But even if your FM patient does not have those issues, consider it a helpful kindness to know where they are. You might just save her an extra trip around the creation looking for the restroom.

## 54. If the FM patient in your life is an avid reader, help her find other ways to read.

Many fibromyalgia patients find it difficult to concentrate on one particular thing for very long. For some FM patients the problem is not one of limited concentration, but of not being able to sit in one place for extended periods. In either case, it can be difficult to read a print book for more than a few minutes at a time.

Some patients find it easier to "read" books in audio form, perhaps in MP3 format so they can carry their player with them when they have to get up and move around the room.

There are a lot of places online to find audio books. You might start your search at your local library. Our local library allows us to freely check out audio books on CD as well as downloadable audio books in various formats. I sometimes check out one, download it to my smart phone and listen to it when it is convenient. There are also a number of web sites where we can download audio books, sometimes free of charge.

My Honey finds it easier to listen to an audio book than to concentrate on reading a printed book. In addition to the easier concentration, she can get up and move around while listening. She has a number of printed books and she owns a Kindle. But the ability to "read" books without having to carry them or stay in one place is a real bonus for her.

## 55. Allow her to take her time when making decisions.

It can be difficult for FM patients to make decisions as basic as whether to bake a cake or watch television. Expect the difficulty and don't give her a hard time over it. It probably frustrates her more than it does you.

This past weekend, I drove my Honey to the mall to order new eyeglasses. The eye exam was uneventful. And although it probably wasn't obvious to anyone else, I could tell that the frame selection process was overloading her a bit too much. The store clerk was standing by her side trying to assist in her selection, unaware that between her suggestions and mine, we were bombarding her with too many choices at one time. To makes matters worse, my Honey was ordering two pairs of glasses and therefore had double the number of frames to decide upon.

I helped her by picking out a few frames that I thought she would like. The clerk helped by telling me whether the frame in question was large enough to hold her tri-focal prescription. In the end we did a "look at this one beside this one" elimination process and got it narrowed down to the two frames that she ordered.

Keep this in mind when shopping or in similar circumstances. Try to avoid situations in which there are a lot of options to choose from when that choice needs to be made in a short period of time. Between fibro fog and potentially pushy salespeople, the possibility for overload is very real.

I need to give myself time to figure things out and make a decision, fortunately I have you (help whenever you do)

## 56. You may have to become a personal taxi driver for her.

Driving can be a challenge for some FM patients. There is the physical difficulty of reaching, shifting gears in some cars, etc. Getting into and out of some cars can be difficult. Having to drive to a place where she has never been or into heavy traffic situations may be daunting and stressful for her.

One challenge that is often overlooked is that FM patients are frequently prescribed a medication that can make driving a dangerous activity for them. The label on the bottle may even state that the patient is not to drive while taking that medication. If you know that your patient should not be driving because of some medication that she has been prescribed, offer to be her taxi driver for the day. You'll do her a favor and potentially prevent an accident at the same time.

# 57. Remember that her symptoms may be different from day to day.

Like air, it's there whether you see it or not. Fibromyalgia has no visibly verifiable signs. Without prior knowledge, you cannot simply look at a person and tell that she has FM. And that is part of the problem that FM patients deal with. People will sometimes look at them and say to themselves, "She looks fine to me. I don't know why she's acting so worn out." If your FM patient is having a good day, her FM may not manifest in an obvious way. If she is having a rough day, you will usually know. That is, if you know your patient well enough to "read" her. Whatever her day has presented her, treat her the same way as you would any other day. Be conscious of her needs and act accordingly.

## 58. Know your FM patient's life needs.

They do not want to be burdensome. They do not like being forced to depend on friends and family for support. But sometimes that dependence is the reality for patients whose FM is severe. If they can't work, income suffers dramatically. If they can't get disability for one reason or another, the desperation is magnified. You may have to offer support in ways other than taxi service. They will not always be candid enough to let you know what their needs truly are. Keep an eye out to be certain your loved one or friend has plenty to eat and that her other critical life needs are somehow met.

## 59. Be mindful that her daily physical care doesn't suffer.

Fibromyalgia is all-consuming to some patients. When it is, life is basically spent surviving the depression, pain, or other effects of the illness. Other health issues may be ignored. Dental care may suffer because of financial restraints or simply because it is ignored in favor of FM. For the same reasons, vision care may be put on the back burner. Fibromyalgia has a way of taking the front and center position in the patient's life. Do what you can to help her take care of her other health-related issues as well.

## 60. Learn to see fibromyalgia as a thief hiding in plain view.

One fibromyalgia patient that I know feels that in some ways, her FM has robbed her of her authority over her own life. She sometimes feels that others regard her as "less" in some ways. When so much of life is out of her hands, it can feel that way.

Your duty, if your family member feels the same lack of authority over her life, is to encourage her and to lift her up. Let her know that she is important, that she is a viable member of her family and her social circle, and that in your eyes, she still rules her own kingdom.

## 61. Help her meet her potential in life.

I know FM patients who once held good paying, fulfilling jobs but lost them because they became unable to perform their duties. Some of the inability is in not being able to physically lift things or to sit or stand for extended periods of time. Sometimes the inability to hold the job is a result of "brain fog" or "fibro fog" that many FM patients experience. It is the same thing that keeps them from concentrating or from reading books. It is that thing that makes it so easy for them to lose keys, cell phones, etc. It is one thing to deal with the fog at home. It is quite another to try to hold a job when you can't concentrate or when your forgetfulness is running at full throttle. Combine fibro fog with the confusion that sometimes stems from sensory overload, and you have a doubly troublesome day at work for the fibromyalgia patient.

Most people have other talents or abilities that are hidden or untapped. Perhaps you can help your FM patient expand her life by helping her explore other interests that she has. If you are in a position to do so, help her find the tools and information that she needs to explore those interests. Maybe there is a work at home opportunity available that would allow her to work at her own pace without the external pressures of demanding people standing over her shoulder. She may just come up with something that could support her financially as well as helping to lift the veil of depression and despair that she feels.

# 62. Help her develop a social network.

Your FM patient may not feel like going out with friends on a given day. She may not be able to sit through movies. She may have a hard time dealing with the noises of life in general. But most people need a social circle of some kind, whether they realize it or not. I personally do not like the idea that a person can build his or her entire social life online. Most people who do that are perfectly capable of physically interacting with their peers. But exceptions exist. If your FM patient just cannot seem to get out into the world enough to develop more friends and relationships that can help her grow socially and help her have a life, then perhaps social networking sites online would be a great alternative.

I know fibromyalgia patients who are not able to walk much or to get out for very long, but they are able to visit with other people to whom they can relate by doing so online. If that is something that she would be interested in, but doesn't know how to get started with it, help her find the information and resources she needs to get online and become a member of forums and networking sites where other members can share her interests.

# 63. Ride the Social Security Disability train with her.

Some fibromyalgia patients have found it difficult to be accepted for disability. In the United States, Social Security Disability claims are handled at the application stage by the individual states. Most states are notorious for disallowing initial claim applications. It can be frustrating or even maddening when medical expenses rise and income doesn't.

Disability approval is neither easy nor categorically impossible. There are attorneys and other companies that specialize in walking disability claims through the system. Some have had a high success rate with fibromyalgia patients. I know some patients who have not been accepted for disability for one reason or another, and I know at least one that has been drawing a monthly disability check from the Social Security Administration for several years.

It is very time consuming and it is not easy at all, but it is possible for some patients to successfully apply for disability, particularly for those who will sign up with a specialist in disability claims. If your FM patient insists on going through the entire claim process alone, all I can say is good luck! In the United States, attorneys or other groups that help applicants wade through the legalities of the system are limited by law in how much they can charge to assist in the claim process. Whatever she has to pay, it will probably be money well spent.

Try to help her find attorneys or organizations to help her with the process. Many, if not most, disability specialists will work on the case and take their fee from the back pay proceeds when the case is finally won. If your patient tries, and just cannot get disability, do what you can to help her deal with that situation. Assure her, if you are sincere in doing so, that you will do whatever you can to get her the best medical care, and that you will do whatever you can to see that she has her personal needs met.

## 64. Find a knowledgeable doctor.

This one may sound like a no-brainer. You might be surprised, though, to learn how many doctors are just not well-informed about it. If that is the case with your FM patient, help her locate a doctor who is knowledgeable enough and interested enough in the study of fibromyalgia to offer her real hope of feeling better.

## 65. Pick up the vacuum cleaner!

Many fibromyalgia patients are unable to do any more than the most basic household chores. For example, my Honey can dust for a while. But even that simple chore can be overdone because of the reaching that frequently results in severe pain. She can do other things that are pretty much at counter-top level. But she cannot handle vacuuming the floor or dusting the ceiling fans. And there are other tasks that, if she does them, she usually pays dearly for later on.

You can help to make your FM patient's life easier by running the vacuum for her. Lift the heavy garbage bag out of the can for her and carry it out for pick up.

## 66. Do away with unnecessary stress at home.

This is vitally important! We all know what a threat stress is to our bodies and minds. Removing stress covers a large territory. Certain foods, divorce, no direction in life, unbalanced life, and not getting enough sleep all contribute to the worst stress.

Stress is like a response to a challenge. But constant challenge is exhausting. If it challenges one of us to do a certain chore, but the other one can do it with his eyes closed, we work it out so that that person does the chore. That saves stress on both parties.

I wrote earlier how it is stressful for my Honey if she cannot get to the right sauce pan with relative ease. Of course, she expects to be able to reach in and take her favorite pan. But stress will take over if she finds it tucked under, say, pans that she hasn't used all week. She kneels down before the kitchen counter and has to unload other pans before she gets to hers. She struggles to stand back up, but now her knees hurt. She has totally lost her peace and is in more pain. With a spot of planning—for example, stopping to grab a stool—this could have been avoided.

Most stress is unnecessary. It takes practice to be able to identify potential sources of stress in the fibromyalgia patient's life. Remember to stay balanced between work, play, rest, and exercise. Too much of any one will stress the mind and body. The imbalance may not be obvious at first to the FM patient, so she may need an occasional reminder. My Honey doesn't watch the clock so there are times that she's been busy far longer than she imagined. That's when I remind her to take breaks and to move about. Movement breaks tension in muscles and releases pain that has built up. My Honey's doctor tells her that it is a good idea for her to move around every thirty minutes or so to keep her body in its most comfortable state.

On days when your fibromyalgia patient is overloaded with pain, try to keep her from having to be around unnecessarily stressful situations. For example, if you need to bring correction to another member of the household, plan that talk outside of the home and not in earshot of the FM patient.

Staying free from stress needs to be a constant goal. Nowadays my honey is slower at getting ready to go out. If she procrastinates and has to hurry to avoid being late, this stresses her big time and makes her nervous. If running late causes us to be tied up in traffic at a time that we are already running late, her body will hold on to tension much longer. At times like this, talk it over. The two of you may decide to just be last and keep the peace, or to just not go.

Disorganization is another big stress producer. Your FM patient might look at her email in-box and see that it's running over, and she is already facing a day full of appointments. It's easy for her to feel overwhelmed. The stress reducing solution might be to work on the in-box as it comes in or in some organized way that it does not have a chance to stack up. Or it might be to purchase one of the software programs on the market that can help to control her in-box. Again, we avoid stress and frustration.

Simplify your life. Slow down. How? Schedule time for you, avoid difficult people and situations if at all possible, and cross off things you do that bring no satisfaction.

We try to make our home "The Stress Free Zone." It may be a worthy goal for you and your FM patient to do the same.

# 67. Accept that getting up is hard to do!

In our house, I am almost always out of bed by 4:00 a.m. or so. The older I get, the less lively I am when my feet first hit the floor. But in general I don't wake up in a groggy state. I can walk upstairs, turn on the computer and instantly get on with whatever it is that I need to do that morning. But for my Honey, getting up is a whole different experience. On most mornings, she is very slow moving, at times barely scooting one foot in front of the other.

I realize that there are many people who aren't morning people. But not being a morning person takes on a different meaning for a person who wakes up with fibromyalgia. She may, and in fact, probably will wake up having great difficulty moving. She's not just slow because her body parts aren't talking to each other yet. She is often in pain from having lain in bed all night.

You should also know that her head is probably nowhere near ready to hear all the things you learned online since you got up. She is not ready for you to read three single-spaced pages of your literary eloquence to her. You might try, but she won't get it. And she may even ask you to stop trying to read to her. It's not rudeness that you are seeing and hearing. It is simply her telling you that the fog hasn't lifted yet and the pain is still sitting front and center.

## 68. Prepare yourself for whatever emotion in her is strongest on that particular day.

The range of emotions that fibromyalgia patients can feel is as wide as it is for any normal person. But they may be more pronounced in the FM patient. She may wake up stiff and feeling pain, yet happy emotionally. She will probably wake up today with some degree of fibro fog, taking it all in stride. But she may also wake tomorrow feeling sad, disappointed, overwhelmed, dreadful, and generally powerless.

If you know your friend or spouse well enough, on such mornings you may also notice a bit of her being embarrassed at feeling so incapable. You may not see her as being generally incapable, but in her life, that feeling is very real. If you sense that she is feeling that way, just be there if she needs you to. Be an encouragement for her, but don't push her. Fibromyalgia patients can use just a little prodding from time to time, but that should never be taken as a license to be pushy, arrogant, or demanding.

If you have a comedic side, try using it (sparingly and judiciously) to point her in a different direction. If you have an idea for some activity that you think may gently take her mind off of how she feels and onto something more enjoyable, then by all means, give it a try. Change your own plans if you need to. It's all a part of being flexible and willing to do whatever it takes to help your FM patient live a more fulfilled life.

## 69. Get involved by keeping your eyes open for new information.

If your fibromyalgia patient is like mine and some others that I am familiar with, she is constantly on the lookout for the next bit of research or testing results that might offer hope to her and others like her. The study of the illness on a personal level can be all-consuming. Perhaps there is an article from a doctor who believes he may have uncovered some potentially life-changing new information. There is the study of new medications hitting the market—studying side effects, real results, marketing push, etc.

She can't do this FM life as easily by herself as she can with your help. If you hear of some new research that you think she might not have heard about, tell her about it. If you hear of a new mattress that you think might offer a better night's sleep, show it to her. She will appreciate your well-researched input.

Do your own research, and then help to get the word out! Like many other illnesses, there is a lack of solid information available about fibromyalgia. Most people have heard the word, but only a small percentage of them have any fact-based knowledge about it. You can help your FM patient by first learning all you can about it, then by helping to spread the word about it. The more support there is, the more likely it is that solid research will continue and real help will be available.

Few things in the life of a person who lives with a disabling illness can bring more hope than the knowledge that someone somewhere is searching for answers and cures. That hope for more effective treatments or even a cure can have a significant positive mental effect on the patient.

Be a partner in her learning process, and consequently a partner in finding the potential for a better, more comfortable life.

# 70. Get involved by occasionally giving her a gentle push.

There is the possibility that some fibromyalgia patients might just give up and accept the pain as being something that can never be alleviated. They may fall into a depressed "funk" that can be very difficult to climb out of. Be on the lookout for such things. Encourage her to get some exercise, even if it is just a slow walk down to the corner and back. Take her out of the house for dinner, a drive through the countryside, or some other mildly adventurous occasion. Exercise is helpful.

Interaction with the outside, in the proper setting and circumstance, can help to lighten the day and return the sparkle to her eyes. And it never hurts to surprise her with a little something. My Honey is probably the easiest lady on the planet to please. She is extremely thankful for even the tiniest expressions of kindness. Perhaps your FM patient is, as well. Next time you see that your spouse or friend is having a dark day, try this. Stop by the flower shop and pick up a simple arrangement in her favorite colors. If she is allergic to flowers or is not really a flower person, pick up something else that you know would normally brighten her day. It could be something as simple as a pack of herbal bath crystals or a small bottle of fragrance.

The point is, sometimes the only thing standing between your FM patient having a dreadful, dark, and lonely day and her having a much better day is for you to just give her a gentle push by showing that you can see she is having it rough right then, and you want to help her have a brighter day. Don't make a big deal of it. Don't announce to the world that you are doing whatever it is that you decide to do just so your patient will feel better. That is shifting the focus from the one who needs the expression of kindness to the one giving it. That is cranking up the ego. Just quietly and tenderly do it without any expectation of praise or exaltation. Then watch her day change.

## 71. Find out what encourages her.

Every one of us has things in life that encourage us, things that lift us up. And every one of us has things that discourage us and push us down. Encouragement comes in many forms. It may be to compliment her on some craft piece that she has strained over. It may be to let her know how much she means to you or how beautiful she is in your eyes. Encouragement gets the feel good chemicals, the endorphins, in our bodies moving, and whenever that happens the potential is there for her pain to decrease for at least a while.

## 72. Do not detach yourself from the problem of fibromyalgia.

Most women are emotionally centered. Most men are physically centered. Men sometimes try to avoid the emotional baggage that can accompany chronic illness by detaching themselves from it. In so doing, they stand off and look at the problem through shaded glasses, not wanting to see the illness—in this case fibromyalgia—for what it is. They do not want to see that their bride or cherished friend is no longer capable of doing the adventurous activities that she did just a few short years earlier. They do not want to see her become a victim of mental fogginess. They do not want to see her in pain or depressed. But, that detachment does absolutely nothing to help her overcome fibromyalgia. And it does nothing for the man looking on.

We are not alone in this world—none of us. Although we may distance ourselves from others, and even feel alone ourselves at times, there is a connectedness that exists between each of us. And when we try to turn that connection off, when we try to act as though we can just make it not be real, we are failing both ourselves and the one we love so dearly. Do whatever you have to in order to overcome that detachment. Read about fibromyalgia. Make it a point to talk to others who are likewise afflicted. Do whatever it takes, even if that means you have to crawl over your pride and your ego on your hands and knees.

## 73. Do not withhold your sympathies from her.

Fibromyalgia patients in general do not want to be smothered with attention. They want to be loved and cared for. They want to be seen as normal, whatever that entails. They also want to know that you are there for them. It is a part of recognizing who they are and what they are going through for you to show sympathy for them. Don't glob it on them like syrup. On some days they cannot handle the personal touch and constant company that you might be to them. But do be there for them with a sympathetic ear and an open heart. On other days that might be just what they need.

## 74. Give her your attention.

I'll be the first to admit that I am not as adept at this one as my Honey needs me to be at times. Sometimes I get hung up looking into that black hole otherwise known as the Internet. I tend to poke my head into whatever it is that I am interested in and keep it there for as long as it takes to satisfy my curiosity. Sometimes that works. And sometimes my attention mechanism needs a bit of tweaking.

Case in point: my Honey and I have a room in our home where we do a lot of our leisure activity. No, it's not a weight room and there is no trampoline in there. There is not even a television in the room. But there is her desk and computer, my desk and computer, my synthesizer and recording equipment and several shelves full of books that could stand to be read. (One would never receive an aerobic workout by following us around.) We frequently are in the room together with me sitting at my computer and her at her computer. I might be completely entranced by something I am reading or writing. She will say something to me and while I hear her talking, I don't hear what she is saying. She may be talking to me and she may be talking to the cat. But I am so wrapped up in my own world that I don't know the difference. It's like seeing someone pass by through the corner of your eye but you have no clue who it was, where they were going, or what they were wearing.

attention to what I need — Love lypes

Need to Love and Give to myself too

It is easy in such cases to allow your spouse's or friend's conversation to be completely peripheral like the person passing by. But it is important to come to the point where you can manage to remove your head from whatever black hole has you in its grips and give your attention to your FM patient when she needs it. Just one more note before you suggest that conversation is a two way street. That is true. Conversation is a two way event. But when fibro fog sets in, when forgetfulness kicks in at full bore, you may have to be the one who takes up the gaps in the conversation.

## 75. Offer your help whenever and wherever it is needed. *Accept help Lyss*

This one may seem obvious to you. It's what we have talked about for the past several thousand words. But what we've not talked about is the ease with which we can fail to see the need to help even it is right in front of us.

It is important for fibromyalgia patients to be as active as they can safely be. My Honey's doctor often tells her that exercise is good for her. But what defines a safe level of exercise varies from one patient to the next. What you consider a good exercise session and what my Honey considers a good workout may be drastically different things.

Many FM patients have other issues that they live with in addition to fibromyalgia. It is common for an FM patient to have arthritis, chronic fatigue, sciatica, depression, and a wide range of other conditions. In fact, they can have fibromyalgia alongside just about any known disease. Such combinations of ailments make life even more difficult for the average FM patient. Be alert for times when you see her doing things that are working against her.

Another example from our own lives would be cleaning the cat's litter box. My Honey takes it upon herself to do it on a daily basis. I hear her in the other room going through the process. I know it is very painful and physically stressing for her. Sometimes I catch the sound of the scooper passing through the litter and call out to my Honey, asking if she wants me to do it. The better thing for me to do would be for me to get off of my butt and walk myself into that room and suggest that she let me take over. Or how about if I just told her that I would be taking on that chore or at least sharing the responsibility with her from now on? There are probably similar things that come up in your life that would be a good place to take over from time to time.

_Don't blame myself for_
_things that happen (yes)_

## 76. Never insinuate blame.

There are people on this planet of ours whose apparent calling in life it is to blame someone for every single thing that comes along. Some of us are unwilling to accept that in real life there are some things that just happen. Sure, if we could retrace every step that precedes every event we might come across something that might, possibly, maybe, somehow have influenced future events in such a way that it might actually have a tiny little something to do with whatever it is that we are dealing with right now. But who needs all that extra brain activity in normal life?

So it is with fibromyalgia. Researchers believe that there are things that could possibly contribute to the start of the illness. There are things that can make its symptoms worse, like stress. But there is absolutely no benefit in trying to place the blame for your FM patient's illness upon her shoulders. Some researchers believe that certain people are born with higher chances of contracting fibromyalgia.

Whatever the research ultimately reveals, it is certain that there is nothing that the patient consciously did to contract fibromyalgia. What person would do so? If you are having difficulty accepting that your spouse or other loved one has fibromyalgia and you see that you misplace your frustration and helplessness by blaming your patient, then do whatever it takes to learn to redirect that energy to something more positive. If you have to, seek out professional help. In blaming the patient for her own disease or illness—whatever it is—you are doing neither yourself nor your FM patient any favors.

*Show myself that I care (yes)*

## 77. Do not withhold your affection.

I believe that even the most hardened people we can think of crave affection on some level. And it is especially true for our loved ones. Not every person expresses affection the same way. Not every person accepts expressions of affection in the same way. But within their being, there is a space that can only be filled with the loving touch and emotion that comes from the truly heart-felt affection of another human.

If you are one of the people in your FM patient's life who you know to be a source of affection for her, don't withhold it from her. I cannot tell you how to show or express that affection. My Honey and your loved one are not the same; no two people are the same. But I can tell you that if it is called for, and you are the one who can be the giver, you will give your patient one of her most cherished gifts by showing her your loving, caring, unconditional affection.

*Sometimes thinking of myself separately might help. How would I treat someone else who has fibro - treat myself that way 124 (yes)*

# 78. Do not demand the impossible.

I know that possibility can be a subjective thing. What is possible for me may not be possible for you. And whatever is possible for you may not be possible for your loved one who has fibromyalgia. There are things that are obviously impossible such as lifting more weight than she is physically capable of lifting. There are other things that are less obviously impossible from time to time—thinking clearly, for instance.

In this scenario, the term impossible is more accurately used to describe activities that either cannot be performed due to physical or mental limitations or that cannot be performed without the real possibility of physical injury. If your FM patient has a severe case of fibromyalgia, you should not expect that upon a moment's notice she will be willing and able to take a five mile hike over a national park trail. She may not be able, and you should not expect her to read in one day, a 250 page book about whatever your interest du jour is. Remember that your possibility and her possibility will most likely not be even close to the same.

Don't demand too much
of myself Cyes or
the inner devel Cyes

# 79. Don't write off the future.

There is something about negativity that tends to take over the space where it is. It has a way of spreading and filling even the cracks and crevices like a poisonous vapor. A negative view of the future as it pertains to your FM patient's life plans can do the same. If you allow your own doubt about her future capabilities and health to contaminate the space that you and she fill, you run a very real danger of getting exactly what you ask for. Your FM patient cannot afford to have you saying and doing things that in essence are writing off her future as a vibrant, healthy person.

There is not one of us alive who can predict with certainty what the future holds. But we know that research is being done that will someday help fibromyalgia patients live more complete and fulfilled lives. There are already a handful of medications that have been approved in the United States for the treatment of certain fibromyalgia symptoms. Scientists are working on other medications that may be able to relieve even more of fibromyalgia's symptoms. Such medications could offer fibromyalgia patients real hope for an active life with little or none of the pain or other symptoms plaguing them.

Researchers are making new discoveries into the possible causes of the illness. Even if the researchers do not discover a definite cause or a definite cure, there is the still very real possibility that your patient could get better. She could go into partial or complete remission. You might say by looking at what is presently known about the illness that such a thing is unlikely. But I would say to you that unlikelihood and impossibility are not even close to the same thing. My Honey has a very severe disabling case of fibromyalgia. At present, her activities are extremely limited when compared to the life she had a few years ago. But neither of us accepts the notion that what we see today is what we will see tomorrow or several tomorrows from now. We are actively making plans for fun things that we will be doing after my retirement, which will be here before we know it. We are looking at our future, not through rose-colored glasses that present us with a fake view of the future, but through hope and an internal knowing that we will be able to once again live an active life together.

Don't write off a future of hope and victory over fibromyalgia, and in the process erase whatever hope your patient has in her heart and mind of waking up one day without pain and with a perfectly clear mind. If you insist on holding such a dim view of the future, then hold it silently within yourself. Please do not poison her world with it.

One day FM patients will be able to travel to conferences far away – alone. They will be able to meet up with friends for an afternoon on the town, comfortably attend college with full course loads, exuberantly compete in singing competitions, and confidently hold jobs in physically and mentally taxing occupations. They will be able to comfortably play the role of soccer mom and all that the title entails.

Until that time, though, it is up to us—the friends, spouses, and other family members—to fill in the gap just a bit and do whatever we can to provide a comfortable, fulfilling life for our FM patients.

# A Final Note

You've seen in this book that life changes dramatically for people after fibromyalgia finds its way into their bodies and their lives. The changes are not what most people would consider positive changes, but they do not have to rob the patient of the joy of living.

Take the information you have read to heart. Add to it whatever you can learn on your own and be there for your friend or family member who has fibromyalgia. If you will implement the suggestions that I have given you, those which are applicable to your FM patient, you will be doing your part to make her life better.

I have a request for you. If you have found this little book helpful, I would appreciate your willingness to help us spread the word. Tell your friends about it. I would also be grateful if you would take a few minutes to go to the book's web page at the seller where you bought it and leave a positive review. Doing so could make it easier for others to learn about the book, too.

Made in the USA
San Bernardino, CA
23 February 2019